THE ADVENTURES OF OTI AND VALENTINA

Oti Moves to California

BY: NICOLA DUCHARME

To my sweet Valentina who makes life so much more fun, and to Paul and Cathy who love Oti almost as much as we do and who take such good care of us all.

Acknowledgements

Thank you to my editor, Melanie Lopata from Get It Write, for all the guidance and support in creating this book. Thank you also to Mikey Burchard for inspiring the images and further helping to shape them. Dan Brumbach, you jumped in and helped with graphics in the final hour, and I am so grateful to you for that. Thank you to Terri Rippee of Rippee Photography for the author bio image. Thank you also to Coco Guerin for sharing your experience and wisdom in creating your books about Belle. (P.S. Finn wants to be in the next one). And to Emma Hass for sharing such amazing and inspiring jumping images on her beautiful Eriel.

Valentina was a young girl who had a big, sweet and sensitive heart, especially towards animals. Even her name, Valentina – like St. Valentine and Valentine's Day – meant *love*.

Valentina was a sassy, energetic and happy girl who saw the world through her big hazel eyes as a fun and inviting place, and she always loved a good adventure.

Valentina enjoyed taking ballet lessons and especially loved performing on stage with fancy costumes. Those performances were the only times she was allowed to wear makeup. What a treat!

She also loved playing with her friends and traveling on planes to other cities and countries. But ponies were her favorite thing of all. Sometimes she dressed up as a cowgirl and pretended that she lived on a ranch surrounded by horses.

Though Valentina loved all animals (she had dogs and bunnies at home!) she loved horses the most. She wanted to ride ponies. She dreamed of ponies and drew pictures of them running in fields with her on their backs, and she even made beautiful crafts of harnesses made of flowers.

When Valentina was two years old, she would ride a sweet and gentle pony named Cookie. Cookie was white with brown spots and had the kindest and most gentle eyes.

Her saddle was tiny because she was a small pony, but she loved to carry kids around the barn. Sometimes Valentina rode her bareback.

By the time Valentina was four years old, Cookie had gotten too old for little girls to ride. She had lost her sight but could still walk around because she knew the barn well, and she trusted the people around her to guide her. Eventually, though, it was too much for her.

Now Cookie enjoyed spending time lounging around eating oats and sweet grass.

Valentina was sad that Cookie couldn't carry her on her back like she used to, but Valentina saw how happy Cookie was able to rest and relax.

Still, Valentina wanted to continue to ride ponies.

Luckily for her, Valentina's mama loved horses as much as she did, and they grew to love them together. Every night, they would snuggle up on the couch and watch movies and television shows about horses and living on a farm. Their favorite was a show called "Heartland." It looked like Heaven, and Valentina and her mama dreamed about having a large barn filled with horses surrounded by a large pasture with big, shady trees. They talked about what it would be like to be able to ride every single day, going on trail rides together and taking lessons in the arena.

One time, Mama and Valentina *did* get to ride together. It was so much fun!

One day, after lots of dreaming and wishing, Mama had a GREAT idea! She thought that maybe - *just maybe* - they could have their own horse. It was a big dream, but big dreams can come true if you want them enough.

Mama had heard of a type of horse called a Gypsy cob. Just like a dog could be a beagle or labrador or even a pug, horses came in different types. Gypsy cobs were very calm and sweet and great for people who were just learning to ride. They are nicknamed the "golden retrievers" of horses, which sounded great to Valentina and her mama because golden retrievers have those same calm, sweet qualities they were looking for in a horse.

They started scouring the internet "horses for sale" pages and found what seemed to be the perfect horse for them. His owner said he was sweet and calm, and maybe a little lazy, which sounded good to them too. Horses are big animals and some of them love to run races or jump big fences. Valentina and Mama didn't want a horse that was too fast for them.

There was just one BIG problem. The Gypsy cob lived in Florida, and that was three thousand miles away from where Valentina and Mama lived. THREE THOUSAND MILES! GULP!!!

They didn't want to miss out on their dream, so the very next day, Mama, Valentina and her daddy hopped on an airplane and flew to Florida to see this special horse. Then they rented a car and drove out to where this wonderful horse lived. Guess what? The moment they saw him, they fell in love!

The horse's name was Otis, but his official name was AWESOME OTIS! He didn't look like an "Otis" to them, and they didn't love his name, but they didn't want to give him a brand-new name. Imagine if someone changed your name when you were five; how confusing would that be? They all thought about it for a while and finally decided on a nickname...Oti!

Oti had a long blond mane like the long beautiful hair of a mermaid. His feet were huge and fluffy with the same beautiful blond hair that hid his hooves. Valentina had never seen such fluffy feet on a horse! He must be able to mop the floor with all that fluff!

Oti's coloring was so unusual; his coat was a deep rich reddish-brown and it had dapples in it, which looked like spots... just like Valentina's freckles on her face!

Oti's coloring was called red roan, meaning his fur was a red and white mixture. Valentina and Mama would later discover that in the summer months, his coat would turn a very light color, almost white, then go back to red in the cooler months, kind of like how Valentina's freckles would appear in the summer and fade in the winter.

His tail almost reached the ground and was a mix of white, golden blond, brown, and black. When Oti rolled in his stall, all the shavings would get stuck in his mane and tail.

Valentina's favorite part was Oti's nose, which was as soft as silk, and he had whiskers that would tickle her nose when she kissed him.

Valentina and her mama both rode Oti that weekend. It was obvious when Valentina rode him that he stepped carefully so as not to hurt or jolt her. He knew he had to take care of her, and he did.

Valentina's mama couldn't stop thinking about Oti. He was just so sweet and funny.

Oti's owner loved him too, but her daughter had a pony named Lollipop, and she couldn't give both horses enough attention; that's why Oti was being sold. He hadn't been naughty, and he wasn't unloved or neglected. In fact, his owner loved him so much that she wanted the best home for him.

So, Oti was Valentina's and her mama's; he was coming to live with them in Southern California!

Oti rode in a truck designed for horses from Florida to California and the trip took two weeks.

The driver of the truck was named Jimmy, and he was kind to the horses. Instead of just driving for days on end across the different states, he let them rest overnight at state parks and barns. The horses were able to stretch their legs, eat hay, and relax before going into the truck again.

In the truck, they had hay and water too. Oti had a stall that was big enough for him to lie down if he wanted to, but mostly he stood up, even to sleep.

Jimmy took very good care of the horses. He messaged Valentina's mama with updates as to where they were and when they'd be arriving, and he even sent pictures of Oti looking happy standing in the fields grazing on lush grass.

Finally, when they arrived and he dropped Oti off, Jimmy joked with Valentina that he might well have kept him because Oti was just like him - relaxed, happy to eat and be left in peace. Everyone laughed about that.

Oti liked Jimmy, but he was very happy to finally be off that truck for the last time and stay with his new family.

Oti soon settled into his new digs. He had a big outdoor stall so he could see the stars and smell the ocean air. He started dreaming...

He truly thought he'd made it to Hollywood and his movie career was just about to begin. You see, Florida had been fun, but Oti really knew he was born to be a star and living in Southern California was the best place for that. He just knew he'd be discovered. He wanted to be as famous as Spirit; maybe they could make a movie together!

Days and weeks went by and Oti realized something: being discovered wasn't easy. He had to WORK most days. Sometimes work was in the arena where he was ridden by his trainer (but he felt super fancy having a trainer of his own).

Sometimes work was lessons with Mama, who wasn't as strict as his trainer but still made him work hard. Sometimes they put him in a round enclosure on a long rope and had him walk around in circles. Oti never understood this; he pretended to be a kite and tried taking off into the air. Other days he just ran and ran because it felt good. Sometimes he just needed to get his wiggles out. I'm sure you can understand that. He was still a young horse, after all, and needed his play time.

Valentina also realized that having her own pony was a lot of work, but she loved it because it was for Oti.

As the long summer days turned to shorter winter days, Oti realized he would need to be in shape and know how to be a good riding horse to get the recognition he deserved in Hollywood.

Now don't be feeling too bad for the poor boy. When she moved him into his barn, Valentina's mama had been worried that he might stand out. After all, many of the other horses were very fancy, were used to being in shows and had traveled all over from Europe with their owners and trainers. Many were worth a lot of money - more than Oti or Valentina could ever imagine. Would Oti feel left out amongst these incredible and talented horses?

Valentina and her mama also worried that they might seem like beginners among all the fancy show jumpers and dressage riders there with years of experience. She worried for weeks for both of them.

But guess what? Nothing could have been further from the truth! As soon as he showed up at the barn, everyone's eyes were on Oti. He became the star attraction at the barn.

His beautiful long and flowing blond mane, his happy tail, and the cute feathering on his legs was so unique and different from the other fancy horses there. No other horse looked anything like Oti, and it set him apart from every other horse.

Oti was also just in-between size; he was taller than the lesson ponies, but shorter than the big, fancy horses. But what he lacked in height he made up for in personality! He was also a very wide horse, and his thick feathered legs showed how strong and sturdy he was.

Valentina could also braid his long mane and his forelock, the part of his mane that went down over his face. That helped to keep him cool on the hot, California summer days.

And when Valentina took his braids out, Oti's mane would fall in beautiful, golden curls. Or Valentina could snuggle on it like a soft pillow of cotton candy.

Oti's coat continued to change color depending on the season: white in the summer and red in the winter. Valentina called him her color-change horse.

But it wasn't just that Oti was good looking; everyone also fell in love with him for his sweet personality. Oti was always in a good mood and was kind and gentle even to the smallest child. He knew Valentina was *his* little girl and he loved to snuggle with her.

He also had a real sense of humor. One day, when Valentina went in to snuggle with him, he grabbed the zipper on her shirt in his mouth and pulled it down! When Valentina and her mama were in his stall, he would always want to be close to them.

He also would stick his tongue out when they tried to take is picture! He was part horse, part clown!

Oti had a friend named Vendi, a beautiful black mare, and he would joke around with her as well...even in the arena. Sometimes it didn't seem like *she* thought it was so funny!

One day, Oti got to dress up as a unicorn which he felt very excited about. He knew then that his new friends and family recognized how special and unique he was.

Oti's head would always stand proud when he walked through the barn next door, passing even the fanciest horses and all the awards hanging on their doors. Everyone would stop and smile, asking if they could pet him and wanting to learn more about this handsome fellow.

You have to wonder if all of this attention went go to Oti's head. It didn't. He tried his little heart out at being the best horse he could be. He might not have been as fit as the other horses, and he might not have known yet how to do all the fancy moves, but you know what? It was FINE because he was young and still learning.

When you're young and still a kid, you're not supposed to know it all or have it all together; you're expected to make mistakes. But if you try hard, and if you are kind to everyone around you and ask for help when you need it, you'll make good friends who want to help and watch you succeed. If you're trying your best, that's all anyone can ever ask.

Oti still thought about being a star in Hollywood from time to time, but he realized that what he dreamed of was right under his nose: being loved and accepted, having lots of yummy food, and many friends - both horses and people. He realized he already was a star in the eyes of those he loved the best and who loved him the best.

Oti was very happy in his stall in Del Mar. He could breathe in the sea air, lay around in the sun, eat all the hay he liked, chat with his horse friends next door, and lap up the attention of his human friends. He even had toys in his stall to play with and a halter with his name on it.

Valentina gave Oti lots of carrots, which he loved, and watermelon which was his favorite. He snuggled Valentina endlessly, which she loved (except when he tried to nibble her hair). He had lots of fresh, soft shavings to roll in, and even Valentina discovered that rolling in fresh shavings felt good!

Best of all, Oti had fallen in love with this little girl named Valentina, *his* Valentina, and he knew that they would be together for many years and have so many adventures together.

Sometimes you realize that your "actual" life is so much better than your "dream" life because it's here and now; it's real. And when a girl whose name means "love" chooses you, you know you are in the right place.

Oti's dreams had come true after all.

ABOUT THE AUTHOR

Nicola Ducharme lives in San Diego, California, with her husband Dave and their daughter Valentina. Nicola is a naturopathic doctor and takes care of people's health for a living. The family's deep love of animals expanded their family to include two dogs, four bunnies, and of course their gorgeous horse, Oti. Nicola has written several books for her work, but when Valentina came along – and then Oti – she knew she wanted to write about them and the very special bond they share.

Can't find Nicola and Valentina? Try the barn; that's where they usually are, or track them down online at www.otiandvalentina.com.

Made in the USA
Las Vegas, NV
11 April 2021